DRESSAGE

Rosie Heywood
Designed by Ian McNee

Illustrated by Mikki Rain
Photographs by Kit Houghton
Consultant: Juliet Mander BHSII

Series Editor: Felicity Brooks
Managing Designer: Mary Cartwright
Additional designs by Susannah Owen

Contents

WHAT IS DRESSAGE?

Dressage is a method of training your pony and improving your riding skills so that you and your pony work well together and understand each other clearly. With practice, dressage should make your pony supple so that his movements remain flowing and natural when you ride him. It should also help to make him more confident and keen to please you.

STARTING DRESSAGE

When ponies are out in the field, they move with light, easy steps. Dressage aims to maintain these flowing movements.

You can start to learn dressage at any time. It doesn't matter how long you've been riding, or what standard you have reached. In fact, you learn some basic skills of dressage, such as how to sit in the saddle correctly, when you first start to ride.

Dressage movements are designed to make your pony strong, supple and balanced. As you continue dressage training, the movements gradually become more challenging for you and your pony.

Although dressage does not involve jumping or riding at high speed, it improves your accuracy and control, which will help with all your other riding activities.

THE HISTORY OF DRESSAGE

The art of teaching horses to obey their riders willingly was first practised by the ancient Greeks over two thousand years ago. In the 16th century, riding schools in Europe trained noblemen in the art of horsemanship. Horses were taught difficult movements which would frighten enemies in battle. Displays of these impressive skills became popular.

In 1735, the Spanish Riding School opened in Vienna, Austria. Modern dressage developed from the teachings of this famous school. The Spanish Riding School is still based in Vienna and its riders and horses continue to perform all over the world.

This horse and rider from the Spanish Riding School are performing a movement called the capriole which was originally used in battle.

DUDLEY SCHOOLS
LIBRARY SERVICE

DRESSAGE COMPETITIONS

Taking part in a dressage competition is a great way to see how well you and your pony are progressing. It also gives you the chance to watch other ponies and riders of different standards. Dressage is a popular sport and there are plenty of competitions and levels to choose from.

Advanced horses and riders make complicated dressage movements look easy, but it takes years of training to reach such a high standard.

POINTS OF A PONY

The different parts of a pony's body are called the "points". These terms are often used in dressage, so it's important to know what they mean.

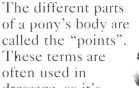

Poll Neck Withers Girth Croup

Shoulder Hindquarters (quarters)

Forehand (front legs) Hindlegs (back legs)

Near (left) foreleg Hock

Knee Near hindleg

Off (right) foreleg Off hindleg

Fetlock Pastern

YOUR POSITION

Developing your riding position is an important part of becoming a dressage rider. A good position will help your pony to keep his balance and make it easier for him to move naturally. Although there's a lot to think about when you work on your position, try to stay relaxed.

ACHIEVING A GOOD POSITION

It takes practice to achieve a good riding position. Even experienced dressage riders continue to work on this part of their riding. Try to stay upright and balanced in the saddle. If you are sitting crookedly, your pony will find it hard to keep his body straight. Ask someone to watch you while you ride. They can then pin-point any problems you may not be aware of. This rider has a good position.

Her head is up and she is looking straight ahead.

Her shoulders are level.

Her back is straight but not stiff.

Her elbows are bent and flexible.

She is sitting in the centre of the saddle, with her weight evenly spread between her seat bones.

The tops of her legs are relaxed.

Her knees are resting gently against the saddle flaps.

Her lower legs are in contact with the pony, next to the girth.

Her heels are lower than her toes.

Her feet are pointing forwards. The balls of her feet are resting on the stirrup bars.

RIDING WITH LONGER STIRRUPS

Dressage riders lengthen their stirrups so that they can ride with straighter legs. Riding with straighter legs means more of your leg is in contact with your pony's sides. This helps you to give lighter, clearer leg aids (see page 6). You'll need to have good balance before you start to ride with longer stirrups.

Your stirrups should be two holes longer than normal. There should be a vertical straight line from your hip to your heel.

In contrast, short stirrups are used for jumping. They help you to lean forward, so your weight is off your pony's back.

IMPROVING YOUR POSITION

One of the best ways to improve your riding position is to have some lunge lessons. The instructor controls your pony with a lunge rein, while you concentrate on keeping a good position. You can also practise riding without reins or without stirrups in lunge lessons. Riding without stirrups is good practice for dressage, as it helps you to prepare for lengthened stirrups.

Try to relax the small of your back and allow your seat to move with your pony.

Cross your stirrups over in front of the saddle so they don't bump against your pony.

Try not to use the reins to balance.

Working without stirrups will improve your sitting trot. This is important since you are not allowed to rise in trot in Elementary dressage tests and above.

EXERCISES ON THE LUNGE

There are lots of exercises you can do on the lunge. The ones described here will loosen your muscles and joints so that you don't become stiff. They will also help to make you more supple, so that you can absorb your pony's cantering and trotting movements through your seat, hips and back. Working on the lunge can be tiring at first, so make sure that you and your pony take frequent breaks.

Put your arms out to the sides and swing around to face each side. Try to keep your legs still. Then do the exercise at a trot, with your hands on your hips.

Keep your feet in the stirrups. Hold the pommel with one hand. Lift your other arm in the air. Swing it backwards in a circle. Repeat with the other arm.

Take your feet out of the stirrups. Bend one leg until you can hold your foot with your hand. Stretch your thigh so your knee points down, then straighten.

USING THE AIDS

You can give signals to your pony which tell him what you want him to do. These signals are called aids, and you give them by using your hands, legs, seat and voice. You can also use artificial aids such as whips and spurs. In dressage, your aids must be as clear and light as you can make them, so that your pony can understand you quickly and easily.

USING YOUR LEGS

To give leg aids, your legs should be relaxed, with your lower legs in contact with your pony's sides. You use leg aids to ask your pony to move forward, to keep him working actively and to tell him where to go. The message you give him depends on where you put your legs and how firmly you use them. To move straight forward, use both legs near the girth. To bend, keep your inside leg on the girth, and your outside leg behind it.

This rider's aids tell her pony to bend to the right. Her legs are well positioned, but her left shoulder and arm should be further forward.

HAND AIDS

You can use your hands to send signals to your pony along the reins to his mouth. Always try to keep the contact with his mouth soft and light. Squeeze your fingers on the reins to slow him down. If you pull hard on your pony's mouth he may start to ignore or resist your hand aids.

Use the inside rein to ask for a bend towards the inside.

Use the outside rein to control your pony's bend and speed.

Outside leg

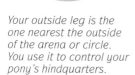

Your outside leg is the one nearest the outside of the arena or circle. You use it to control your pony's hindquarters.

Your inside leg is the one nearest the middle of the arena or circle. You use it to ask your pony to bend towards the inside and move with impulsion.

Inside leg

Tips for giving aids
● To give clear aids you must be well balanced, and in a good position.
● If your pony does not respond, check that you are giving the correct aids.
● Try to keep your hands, legs and seat still when you are not using them.
● Try to use your aids as sensitively as possible, so that your pony remains responsive to you.
● Try not to give your pony conflicting aids such as pulling on the reins when you are using your legs to ask him to go forward.

SEAT AIDS

Your seat and body can be used to slow your pony down. On a correctly-trained pony, they can also be used to create more impulsion and to ask your pony to bring his hindlegs further underneath him. Your seat and body should be in balance with your pony, so that you don't tip forwards or backwards.

USING YOUR VOICE

You're not allowed to use your voice in dressage tests, but you can use it to reinforce other aids while you're training. Your pony understands the way you say words, rather than the words themselves. Quick, high-pitched commands will keep him active, while slow, low-pitched commands will slow him down.

To slow your pony down, sit tall, with your weight down into your heels.

Try to sit still. If you move around, your pony may become confused.

DRESSAGE WHIPS

If your pony ignores your leg aids, you can use a whip to emphasize what you mean. Give your pony the correct leg aid first. If he doesn't respond, tap him with the whip just behind your leg. If you're using a standard whip, put the reins in one hand, so you can use the other hand to apply the whip without pulling on the reins.

Standard whip

Dressage whip

Dressage whips are longer than standard whips, so you can use them without taking your hands off the reins.

Hold your whip in your inside hand.

SPURS

Spurs are worn by experienced dressage riders to give light leg aids. Riders only start to use spurs when they have developed a good leg position and are able to keep their legs still, so that the spurs never touch the pony by mistake.

The shank of the spur should be no longer than 3cm.

Only blunt spurs can be worn in Pony Club dressage tests.

7

THE PACES

Your pony can walk, trot, canter and gallop. These different steps are called his paces. In dressage tests, you will be asked to show how well your pony moves in each pace, except gallop. Before you can begin to improve your pony's paces you will need to understand how he moves in each one.

MOVEMENTS IN WALK

Your pony walks by moving his legs one at a time. On a hard surface, you should be able to hear four separate sounds, called beats, as each hoof hits the ground. His hindlegs should step into the marks left by his forelegs. This is called "tracking-up". With training, his hindlegs should "over-track" and step over the marks of his forelegs. If a pony moves two legs at the same time, he is pacing rather than walking. This is a serious fault. A pony may pace if he wasn't trained properly when he was young, or if his rider keeps the reins too short.

Beat one　　*Beat two*　　*Beat three*　　*Beat four*

Off hindleg hits the ground.　　*Off foreleg*　*Near hindleg*　　*Near foreleg*

MOVEMENTS IN TROT

When your pony trots, he moves his legs in diagonal pairs. As he springs from one pair of legs to the other, there is a moment when all his legs are in the air. This is called "the moment of suspension". Your pony's trot should have a regular rhythm and his hindlegs should track-up into the marks of his forelegs. The speed of your pony's trot is important. If he trots too fast he won't have time for the moment of suspension. If he's too slow, he will start to drag his feet.

Beat one　　　　　　*Beat two*

Off hindleg　*Near foreleg*　　*Near hindleg*　*Off foreleg*

The pony's off hindleg and near foreleg hit the ground at the same time.

All the pony's legs are in the air for the moment of suspension.

His near hindleg and off foreleg then hit the ground at the same time.

Another moment of suspension follows, then the sequence continues.

CANTER

There should be three quick beats to your pony's canter, followed by a moment of suspension when all his feet are in the air. Your pony should canter with even, relaxed strides. Most of his weight should be on his hindlegs, which should step well under his body. A lazy pony may lose the moment of suspension or move his inside hindleg and outside foreleg separately instead of together.

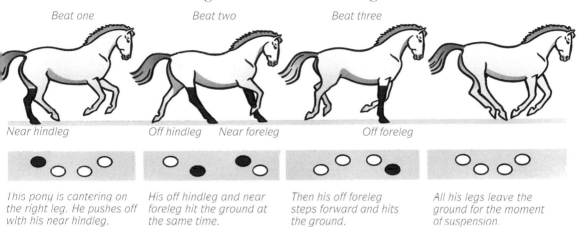

Beat one *Beat two* *Beat three*

Near hindleg *Off hindleg* *Near foreleg* *Off foreleg*

This pony is cantering on the right leg. He pushes off with his near hindleg.

His off hindleg and near foreleg hit the ground at the same time.

Then his off foreleg steps forward and hits the ground.

All his legs leave the ground for the moment of suspension.

DIFFERENT TYPES OF WALK, TROT AND CANTER

Dressage ponies can vary the length of their steps in each pace without altering their speed. It's hard work for ponies to shorten or lengthen their paces and it takes careful training. The ultimate shortened and lengthened paces are called "collected" and "extended". You can learn about them on pages 16 and 17.

This pony is stretching his neck well forward for the free walk.

In medium trot, the pony stretches out his body to take longer steps.

Walks

Your pony's normal walk is called "medium walk". In Preliminary and Novice dressage tests you may also be asked to show "free walk". For free walk, give your pony a long, but not slack, rein so he can stretch out his back and neck and take longer steps. He should move forward actively, without slowing down.

Trots and canters

Your pony's normal trot and canter are called his "working" trot and canter. In Preliminary and Novice dressage tests you will have to show that your pony can take slightly longer steps than in his working paces. This is the first stage towards "medium" trot and canter, in which your pony lengthens his stride.

WAY OF GOING

A pony's "way of going" is the way he moves. If your pony is going well and working correctly he will be feeling relaxed and happy. You will also find him comfortable to ride. Here are some important points which will affect your pony's way of going.

KEEPING YOUR PONY STRAIGHT

Your pony should be able to keep straight in all his paces. This means that his hindlegs should follow in the tracks of his forelegs and not swing out to the sides. His body should be straight from the tip of his nose to his tail, or gently curved if you are riding a circle. If your pony isn't straight, it may be because you are riding crookedly, or because you have stronger contact on one rein.

This pony has started to shift his body to the right because his rider is sitting crookedly.

It could also be because your pony is not responding to your aids properly. Lunging exercises (see page 5) will help you to sit straight, while transitions (see page 12) will help to make your pony "listen" to your aids. Practise riding straight lines across the schooling area so that your pony doesn't start to rely on the edge of the school to keep himself straight.

STAYING CORRECTLY BALANCED

To be correctly balanced, your pony must be moving forward actively (with lively steps) in response to your aids. He must be working with plenty of impulsion (see next page) from his hindquarters. If he starts to rush he may lose his rhythm and put more weight on his forehand. He may start to use the reins to balance, and he'll be more likely to trip. A pony who is well balanced is said to be in "self carriage".

Rhythm and tempo

- Rhythm is the regularity of your pony's footfalls. When his rhythm is steady, his balance will be good.
- Tempo is the speed of your pony's rhythm. In dressage, your pony's tempo should stay constant.

Hillwork when you're out hacking is an excellent way to improve your pony's balance.

CREATING IMPULSION

Impulsion is the energy your pony uses to move forward. When you use the aids to control this energy, your pony will take lighter, springier steps. His hocks will engage, which means he'll put more of his weight onto his hindquarters and use his hindlegs to push himself along. His hindlegs will step further underneath his body.

The pony in front is moving with impulsion. His hindlegs are underneath him and his hocks are engaged.

The hocks of the pony behind are not engaged.

ACCEPTING THE BIT

When your pony accepts the bit, he will willingly move forward until he can feel a light but steady contact between the reins and the bit in his mouth. You will be able to feel this contact too. There should be no resistance to the bit in his mouth, neck or back. His outline (the shape his body makes) should become rounder. A pony won't accept the bit until he is straight, balanced and moving with impulsion.

This pony has accepted the bit and his outline is well rounded. His back and loins are supple and relaxed.

The pony's neck is gently curved from the withers to the poll and his jaw is relaxed.

This pony is not accepting the bit. His outline is "hollow" and his ears are back as a sign of resistance.

His tail is soft and swinging.

Helping your pony to accept the bit
- Use your legs to push your pony firmly forwards.
- Keep your hands still.
- Don't try to make contact by pulling on the reins.
- As soon as your pony accepts the bit, relax your aids slightly to reward him.

11

TRANSITIONS

A transition is a change of pace, such as from walk to trot, or from working trot to medium trot. Transitions teach your pony to pay attention to your aids and help to improve his balance and impulsion. They are included in all levels of dressage, from Preliminary to Advanced.

UPWARD TRANSITIONS

Upward transitions increase the pace, for example, from walk to trot. Before you ask for an upward transition, make sure your pony is attentive and moving well.

Sit lightly in the saddle. Close your legs on your pony's sides by the girth. Follow his head movements with your hands but don't lose contact with his mouth.

Walk

Let your body move forward with your pony. This will help you to balance in the next pace.

Trot

UPWARD TRANSITION TO CANTER

Your pony should canter with his inside leg leading. Go into sitting trot before you ask for canter. Use your inside leg on the girth and your outside leg behind the girth. This tells your pony to start, or "strike off", with his outside hindleg, so that his inside foreleg leads the canter (see page 9). Asking for canter as you go around a corner will encourage your pony to start with the correct leg.

This pony is cantering with the correct, inside leg leading.

DOWNWARD TRANSITIONS

Don't pull on the reins to slow your pony down. It's uncomfortable for him.

Downward transitions slow the pace. To ask for one, sit taller in the saddle, with your weight down in your heels. Keep your legs lightly on your pony's sides. Close your fingers around the reins and squeeze. Stop squeezing when he responds.

DOWNWARD TRANSITION TO HALT

When your pony halts, he should stand straight and square. This means that he has equal weight on each leg, and that his front and back legs are in line. He should be able to keep still, without fidgeting or shuffling about. Keep a light rein contact during the halt, so that he stays alert, waiting for your next command.

Stepping back

Crooked halt

Resisting

Don't try to force your pony to stop by pulling the reins.

If your pony steps back, it may be because your hand aids are too strong. Lighten your hold as soon as he stops, but don't let the reins go loose.

If your pony's halt is crooked, make sure your left and right aids are even. Try placing two poles on the ground and halting between them.

If your pony resists the halt, it may be because your aids were unclear, or because your pony was not moving well before the halt. Try to use clear aids.

USING THE HALF-HALT

In dressage tests you will be asked to change pace at specific markers. Giving a half-halt is a good way to prepare your pony for transitions.

This rider should have a little more weight in her heels.

A half-halt is a set of aids which warn your pony that you're about to ask him to do something different, such as change pace. It also tells him to engage his hindquarters and hocks. Half-halts can be used in all paces, but practise in trot first. Sit tall in the saddle and put your weight into the stirrups. Close your legs around your pony's sides and close your fingers on the reins so that they restrain him.

CIRCLES AND TURNS

Dressage tests consist of a series of circles, turns and transitions. These movements are designed to show off your pony's ability and training. More advanced dressage tests involve smaller circles and tighter turns. With regular practice, you and your pony's suppleness and balance will improve so that you can start to ride smaller, more precise shapes.

HOW A DRESSAGE PONY BENDS

When a pony bends correctly, he curves his whole body, from his tail to his poll (the top of his head). His outside hindleg steps into the same track as his outside foreleg, while his inside hindleg steps well underneath his body. He is well balanced, his rhythm and tempo stay the same and his body has a rounded outline. He looks in the direction he's going and doesn't bend his neck towards the outside.

This pony is bending correctly. His whole body is bending along the curve of the circle.

This pony is bending incorrectly. His shoulders are "falling-out" from the curve of the circle.

AIDS FOR BENDING

Keep your head up and look in the direction you are going.

To help your pony keep his balance, turn your body so that your shoulders are in line with his shoulders.

To encourage your pony to bend his whole body, use your inside leg on the girth. Use your outside leg behind the girth to control his hindquarters. Squeeze and release the inside rein to make sure your pony bends his neck. Use your outside hand to control his speed and stop his neck bending too much.

Your pony may be stiff on one side and find it harder to bend that way. You will need to work this "stiff rein" a little harder to loosen it. Start your training sessions with circles on his easier rein before you change to his stiffer side.

Bending terms

A change of direction is called a change of rein.

A circle or bend to the right (in a clockwise direction) is called a circle or bend on the right rein.

A circle or bend to the left (in an anti-clockwise direction) is called a circle or bend on the left rein.

RIDING CIRCLES IN THE ARENA

The picture below shows how a Pony Club dressage arena is laid out. Letters are placed at specific points around the outside. Because they are in the centre, the letters D, G and X are not marked in the arena. When you ride a test, you will be asked to begin each circle at a particular letter. You may be asked to ride a 20m circle, a 15m circle, or a 10m circle, which is the most advanced.

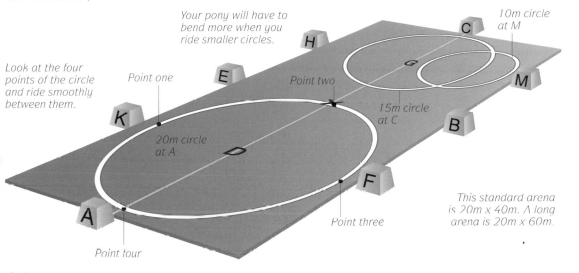

Your pony will have to bend more when you ride smaller circles.

10m circle at M

Look at the four points of the circle and ride smoothly between them.

Point one

Point two

15m circle at C

20m circle at A

Point three

This standard arena is 20m x 40m. A long arena is 20m x 60m.

Point four

Other dressage shapes

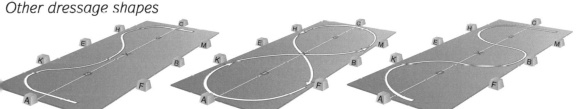

Shallow loops involve a slight bend.   *Figures-of-eight change the rein.*   *Serpentines are a series of loops.*

TURNS IN THE ARENA

In dressage, a bend from one straight line to another is called a turn. You will need to concentrate hard to turn accurately. The most difficult turn is onto the centre line. Practise riding it from both directions.

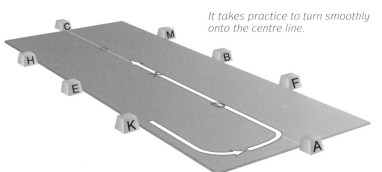

It takes practice to turn smoothly onto the centre line.

Centre line turns
- Look down the centre line before you start to turn onto it.
- Ride the turn with an even bend, then straighten up by using equal rein and leg contact on your pony's sides.
- Look straight ahead and sit centrally in the saddle.
- If your pony drifts left, use your left leg to push him back to the centre.

15

COLLECTING AND EXTENDING

Dressage ponies can take longer or shorter steps in each pace, while keeping the same rhythm and tempo. This is called extending and collecting. You can start to collect and extend when, as a result of transition and circle work, your pony has become supple, balanced and responsive. Walk is the hardest pace to collect or extend, so begin training in trot and canter.

COLLECTED PACES

In collected paces, the pony takes shorter, higher steps. He covers less ground with each step, so that in trot and canter, the moment of suspension is more pronounced. The movement of the pace has an upward, rather than a forward, feel. The rider stays in sitting trot.

This pony is in a good collected trot. The rider is well positioned and is sitting lightly in the saddle.

The pony's head is almost vertical.

His neck is raised and arched.

Most of the pony's weight is on his hindquarters, so that his forelegs are "light".

His hocks are well engaged and his outline is rounded.

He is bending his legs well to make his steps higher.

WORKING TOWARDS COLLECTION

Your pony will be expected to show the first stages of collection in Elementary dressage tests. At each test above Elementary, a greater degree of collection will be required.

It's difficult for your pony to collect his paces. Ask him to shorten his steps for a few strides at first, then push him into his working pace.

The aids for collection
- Close your legs around your pony's sides so that he moves forward with impulsion.
- At the same time, close your fingers on the reins to contain your pony's forward movement.
- Listen to your pony's rhythm and tempo. They should stay the same.

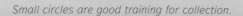

Small circles are good training for collection.

EXTENDED PACES

In extended walk, trot and canter the pony takes long strides. In extended walk and trot, his hind-feet over-track. In order to extend, the pony has to stretch out his body, which gives him a longer outline. His tempo and rhythm should stay the same.

This pony is in a good extended trot. He is moving with impulsion and his outline is long and rounded.

His hindquarters are well engaged and he is light on his feet.

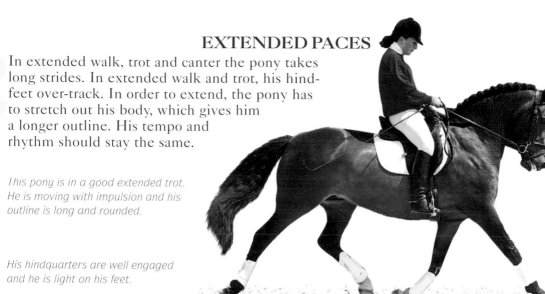

LEARNING TO EXTEND

Try extending in trot first. Use rising trot at first, as this will encourage your pony to take longer steps. Collect your pony's trot on the short side of the arena then use the extending aids (see below) as you go up the long side. Only ask for four or five lengthened strides at first, so he doesn't lose his balance, or start to take faster, shorter steps.

This pony is not extending well. His outline is "hollow". His hindquarters are not well engaged.

The aids to extend

● Use your legs to make your pony move with more impulsion.
● Let your hands follow the movement of his head and neck, so that he can lengthen his outline.
● Don't let the reins go loose, or he'll go faster.

● Make sure his rhythm and tempo stay the same in the extended pace.
● Only ask for a few extended steps at first.
● Work towards medium trot (see page 9) before you ask your pony to extend his trot fully.

COUNTING STRIDES

You can check whether your pony is extending and collecting by counting his strides. Count the number of strides he takes between two markers in working trot and canter. Ride between the markers again, asking your pony for collection or extension. Count his strides in each pace.

Ponies should take more strides when they collect and fewer strides when they extend

Your pony's rhythm and tempo should stay the same.

LATERAL WORK

In lateral work, a dressage pony moves his body sideways, so that his hindfeet do not follow in the tracks of his forefeet. There are several different lateral movements, some of which are included in dressage tests. Others are not included in tests, but are useful training exercises for you and your pony.

TURN ON THE FOREHAND

To do a turn on the forehand, a pony moves his hindlegs around to the side, while his forelegs stay in the same place. He should keep the same sequence of footfalls as in walk (see page 8), so that his forelegs mark time on the spot. His hindlegs should cross over each other as he moves them. Turn on the forehand is not asked for in tests, but it's a good introduction to lateral work.

Start with a quarter (90°) turn. Build up to a half (180°) turn, as shown here.

Aids for turn on the forehand
- Turn into the middle of the arena and establish a good halt.
- Use your inside leg firmly on the girth to ask your pony to move his hindquarters to the side.
- Keep your outside leg lightly behind the girth.
- Use your inside rein to encourage your pony to look towards the inside.
- Use your outside rein at the same time as your inside leg, to stop your pony from moving forward.

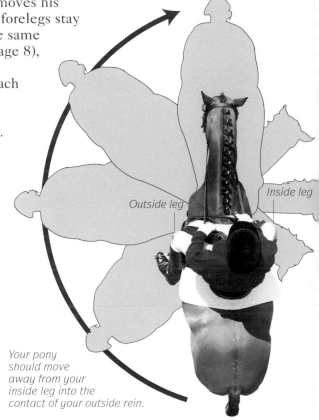

Outside leg

Inside leg

Your pony should move away from your inside leg into the contact of your outside rein.

POSSIBLE PROBLEMS

If your pony walks forward, face the edge of the arena when you practise.

If your pony resists you, he may need more practice at circles and turns, or your aids may be unclear. If he starts to step back, use firmer leg aids, and lighten your hand aids.

If he walks forward, you may be asking for too many steps too early, or your aids may be incorrect. If he bends his neck too much, lighten the inside rein and use the outside rein to control the amount of bend.

DEMI-PIROUETTES

To do a demi-pirouette, a pony moves his forelegs in a half circle around his hindlegs. He begins from a collected walk and puts his weight on his hindquarters to move his forelegs. Demi-pirouettes are harder for a pony than a turn on the forehand.

Give your pony a half-halt before you give him the aids for a demi-pirouette. Ask for a quarter turn at first. It's better if your pony makes a small half circle with his hindlegs rather than stepping back, which is a serious fault.

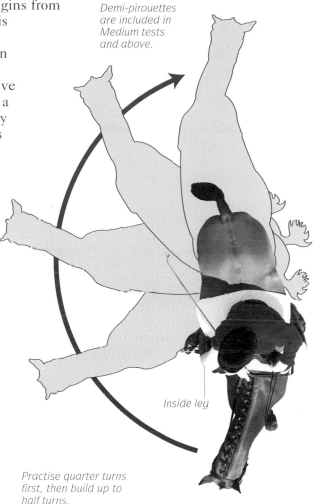

Demi-pirouettes are included in Medium tests and above.

Your pony's body should bend slightly in the direction he's going.

When you have completed the movement, always walk your pony forwards.

Aids for demi-pirouettes

- Half-halt to collect your pony's walk.
- Use your inside leg on the girth to maintain inside bend and impulsion.
- Use your outside leg behind the girth to control your pony's hindquarters.
- Use the inside rein to ask your pony to bend towards the inside.
- Use the outside rein to control his speed and stop him from moving forwards.
- Use the outside rein close to your pony's neck and the inside rein away from it to encourage him to move his forehand around.

Inside leg

Practise quarter turns first, then build up to half turns.

COMMON FAULTS

If your pony's quarters swing out to the side, use your outside leg more firmly to control them.

Outside leg

If your pony stops moving his inside hindleg or loses the correct sequence of footfalls, use your inside leg to increase his impulsion. Don't ask for too many steps at first, and walk him forwards when you finish the movement.

If he steps back, you may be using too much outside rein. If he doesn't bend his body, ask for more bend in preparation, and use more inside leg and inside rein.

LEARNING TO LEG-YIELD

In leg-yield, a pony moves forwards and diagonally sideways at the same time. His body should be straight, apart from his head, which should bend slightly away from the direction he's travelling in. You won't be asked to leg-yield in a dressage test, but it's a useful exercise because it teaches your pony obedience and balance. It also helps you to co-ordinate your aids and use them sensitively.

Aids for leg-yielding

- Use your inside leg firmly on the girth to move your pony sideways.
- Use your outside leg gently behind the girth to move him forwards and stop his hindquarters from swinging out to the side.
- Use the inside rein gently to ask your pony for a slight inside bend at his poll.
- Use the outside rein firmly to steady your pony.
- Keep your weight central and try to stay in an upright, balanced position.

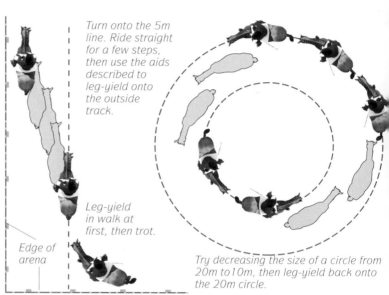

Turn onto the 5m line. Ride straight for a few steps, then use the aids described to leg-yield onto the outside track.

Leg-yield in walk at first, then trot.

Edge of arena

Try decreasing the size of a circle from 20m to 10m, then leg-yield back onto the 20m circle.

SOLVING LEG-YIELDING PROBLEMS

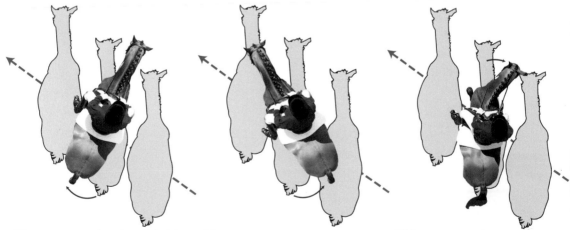

If your pony leads with his quarters, he probably lacks impulsion. Ensure you are riding straight before you ask for leg-yield, and ride him firmly forwards.

If your pony trails his quarters and leads with his shoulders, use more outside rein. Use your inside leg further back to push his quarters over.

If he bends his neck too much, ease the contact with the inside rein. Ride him forward with plenty of impulsion to keep him straight in the leg-yield.

WHAT IS SHOULDER-IN?

When riding shoulder-in, a pony moves forward, with his body bent away from the direction he's travelling in. You'll be asked to ride shoulder-in in Elementary dressage tests and above. Practising shoulder-in encourages your pony to engage his inside hindleg, making it easier for him to learn collection (see page 16).

When a pony performs shoulder-in, he makes three separate tracks with his feet.

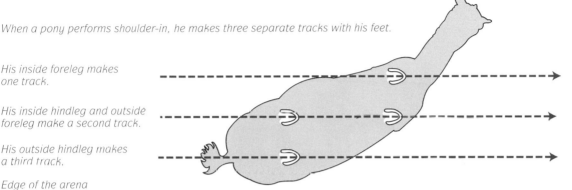

His inside foreleg makes one track.

His inside hindleg and outside foreleg make a second track.

His outside hindleg makes a third track.

Edge of the arena

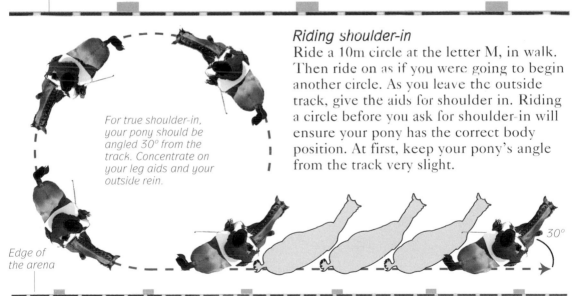

For true shoulder-in, your pony should be angled 30° from the track. Concentrate on your leg aids and your outside rein.

Edge of the arena

Riding shoulder-in

Ride a 10m circle at the letter M, in walk. Then ride on as if you were going to begin another circle. As you leave the outside track, give the aids for shoulder in. Riding a circle before you ask for shoulder-in will ensure your pony has the correct body position. At first, keep your pony's angle from the track very slight.

Aids for shoulder-in

● Use your inside leg on the girth to ask your pony to turn his body towards the inside.
● Use your outside leg behind the girth to prevent his quarters from swinging outwards.
● Use the inside rein very gently to reinforce the amount of bend.
● Use the outside rein to control the amount of bend and the speed.

Common problems with shoulder-in

● If your pony lacks impulsion, use your inside leg more firmly and check that he has not bent inwards too much.
● If your pony varies the amount he bends, check you have the right balance between your inside leg and outside rein.
● If he is bending his neck too much, use more outside rein and less inside rein.
● If his quarters fall out, use your outside leg more firmly to control them.

EXERCISES IN CANTER

In Preliminary and Novice dressage, your pony should canter with his inside foreleg leading. This is known as "true canter" or being "on the correct leg". If you change the rein (see page 14), you must ask your pony to change his leading leg, so that he stays in true canter. Your pony's true canter should be well balanced on both reins.

WALK TO CANTER, CANTER TO WALK

This pony and rider are practising walk to canter and canter to walk transitions.

Transitions are good preparation for simple changes of leg (see below).

For walk to canter, make sure your pony has plenty of impulsion. Ride a 10m circle as preparation. This will help your pony to engage his inside hindleg and help you to place your aids correctly. Use clear, firm canter aids when you are ready for the transition.

For canter to walk, ride a couple of steps of trot before you walk. This is called a progressive transition. Collect the canter first and keep your lower legs on your pony's sides to maintain the collection and impulsion. Use light hand aids when you ask for the transition.

SIMPLE CHANGE OF LEG

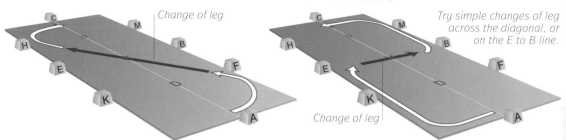

Change of leg

Try simple changes of leg across the diagonal, or on the E to B line.

Change of leg

A "simple change of leg" is when a pony changes his leading leg in canter by trotting (or when more advanced, walking) for a few steps, then cantering again with his other leg leading. To ride a simple change of leg, use the canter aids (see page 12) to canter. To change your pony's leg, ask him to trot for three or four strides. Then use the canter aids again, but with your other leg behind the girth.

Possible problems

● If your pony resists your aids, he may not be ready for simple changes. Practise general transition work.
● If your pony pulls on the bit or trots faster, try simple changes on the E to B line so he has less room to speed up.
● If your pony canters with one leg leading in front and the opposite behind he is "disunited". Go back to walk or trot.

BEGINNING COUNTER CANTER

Counter canter is the opposite of true canter. The pony uses his outside leg to lead, with his body slightly bent towards the leading leg. He needs to be obedient so he resists his natural impulse to lead with the inside leg. Counter canter will improve a pony's suppleness and balance, because he'll have to use different muscle combinations. Try the exercises below to introduce him to this difficult movement.

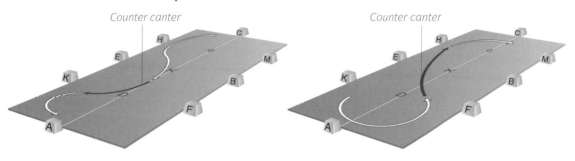

Counter canter

Begin by cantering with the inside leg leading. As you reach the long side of the arena, ride a shallow loop. When your pony turns back into the outside track he will be counter cantering for a few strides.

This dressage rider is performing a balanced, steady counter canter.

As his balance improves, canter a 15m half circle at the end of the arena. Turn back onto the track, so that your pony is in counter canter. Maintain the counter canter to the quarter marker.

Keeping balanced
If your pony breaks into a trot or changes his leading leg, he may have lost his balance. Here's how to prevent this.
- Introduce your pony to counter canter gradually.
- Ride shallow loops smoothly.
- Try not to move suddenly in the saddle.
- As you turn back towards the outside track, keep your aids the same.

SADDLERY AND DRESS

When you enter a dressage test, read the rule book carefully to find out what you and your pony should wear. On the day, groom your pony thoroughly, and check that your clothes are clean and tidy. Knowing that you both look your best will boost your confidence when you enter the arena.

WHAT TO WEAR FOR DRESSAGE TESTS

This saddlery and dress should be suitable for most Preliminary, Novice and Elementary tests, but always double-check in the relevant rule book.

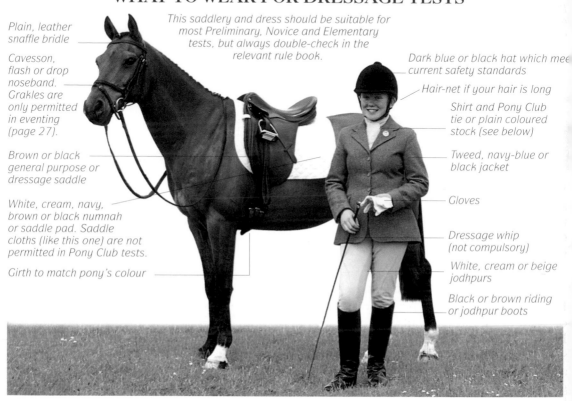

Plain, leather snaffle bridle

Cavesson, flash or drop noseband. Grakles are only permitted in eventing (page 27).

Brown or black general purpose or dressage saddle

White, cream, navy, brown or black numnah or saddle pad. Saddle cloths (like this one) are not permitted in Pony Club tests.

Girth to match pony's colour

Dark blue or black hat which meets current safety standards

Hair-net if your hair is long

Shirt and Pony Club tie or plain coloured stock (see below)

Tweed, navy-blue or black jacket

Gloves

Dressage whip (not compulsory)

White, cream or beige jodhpurs

Black or brown riding or jodhpur boots

HOW TO TIE A STOCK

This bit of the stock goes at the front of your neck.

Pull the loose ends into a knot.

Stock pin

Put the middle of the stock on the front of your neck. Wrap the ends around your neck. If there is a loop on the stock, feed one end through it at the back.

Pass the right end over and under the left. Pull tight. Form a loop with the left end as shown. Pass the right end over and through the loop. Pull into a knot.

Arrange one end of the stock neatly over the other, so the knot is hidden. Secure the ends together with a plain stock pin, fastened horizontally.

PLAITING YOUR PONY'S MANE

You don't have to plait your pony's mane for a Pony Club test, but it does make him look smart. It also helps the judge to see the shape of his neck. You will need some rubber bands, a needle and thread, some white plastic tape and a mane comb. Sew the plaits as shown below. Either plait or pull your pony's tail. Don't plait your pony's mane and tail if he's a Native breed or an Arab.

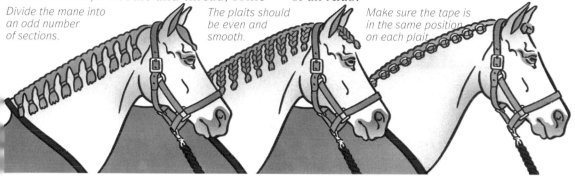

Divide the mane into an odd number of sections.

The plaits should be even and smooth.

Make sure the tape is in the same position on each plait.

Split the mane into sections three-quarters of the width of your comb. Comb each section and fasten with a rubber band.

Take the rubber band off the first section. Split into three parts. Plait them together. Sew the end of the plait to secure it.

Fold the plait under twice. Sew it into place. Wrap white plastic tape around the end of the plait. Make one plait from the forelock.

ADVANCED DRESSAGE

In Advanced dressage, riders use dressage saddles and double bridles. Dressage saddles have long, straight saddle flaps. The girth tabs are also long, while the girth is short, so that the buckles do not sit under the saddle flaps. This helps the rider to keep his or her legs close to the pony's sides.

Double bridles have two bits, and two sets of reins. They give the rider more control over the pony's action.

Top hat

Rider's number tied on bridle

This Advanced dressage rider is competing in an International competition.

Tailcoat

Dressage saddle

White saddle cloth showing rider's nationality

Double bridle

Dressage girth

DRESSAGE COMPETITIONS

As well as being exciting and challenging, dressage competitions are a good way of seeing how your training is progressing. In a competition, you will have to perform a four-to five-minute dressage test, consisting of various different movements. The best way to find out about competitions in your area is from your local riding school or Pony Club branch.

WHICH TEST TO ENTER

DRESSAGE TEST		Max marks
Order Marker Movement / Pace		
1. A	Enter at medium walk	10
X	Working trot	10
2. C	Track left	
A	Circle left 20 metres diameter	
3. Between		10
A & F	Working canter left round the arena	
to K		10
4. Between		
K & A	Working trot	
5. Between		
M & C	Medium walk	
H X F	Change rein in free walk on a long rein	10
F	Medium walk	
6. Between		10
A & K	Working trot	
C	Circle right 20 metres diameter	
7. Between		10
C & M	Working canter right round the arena	
to H		10
8. Between		10
H & C	Working trot	10
9. K X M	Change rein in working trot	
10. H X F	Change rein in working trot	
11. A	Turn down centre line	
After X	Medium walk	10
G	Halt, stand still and salute	
Leave arena at walk on a long rein at A		
		10
		10
12.	General impression	10
13.	Obedience	10
14.	Position of rider	
15.	The correct use and effect of the aids	
		Total 150

Dressage tests are divided into six levels: Preliminary, Novice, Elementary, Medium, Advanced Medium and Advanced. Riders start competing at Preliminary level. There will be several different tests to choose from in your level. Send off to the competition secretary for a schedule and the test sheets. Read them carefully before you decide which test to enter. Choose a test that has movements you know you can do well. The competition schedule will tell you when to ring the secretary to find out what time your test starts.

Test sheets
Test sheets tell you:
● The order in which you should ride the movements.
● The marker at which you should start each movement.
● What each movement should be.
● The pace in which you should carry out each movement.
● The maximum number of marks the judge can give you for each movement.

LEARNING THE TEST

Once you've decided on a test, try to learn it by heart. Some competitions let you have a "commander" who calls out what comes next, but it's better to rely on memory. To help you, draw the test out on paper. Go through the movements in your head too. Imagine how you could avoid possible problems. Practise the movements on your pony, but not always in the right order. If he learns the test, he may try to start the next movement before you reach the correct marker.

Try marking out a mini-arena on the ground so you can learn the test by walking it.

ARRIVING AT THE SHOWGROUND

Make sure you arrive at the showground in good time, as there is a lot to do before you compete. Settle your pony out of the wind, in the shade if it is hot. Leave someone experienced in charge, while you go and check in with the secretary. Find out which arena you will be competing in and confirm your number and start time. Also find out where you can ride in (see page 28).

It's a good idea to watch some of the other competitors in your class, as you may pick up some useful tips.

EVENTING COMPETITIONS

Eventing competitions give you a chance to practise your jumping skills.

You could also enter an eventing competition, which includes cross-country and show jumping as well as dressage. Eventing requires all-round skills and stamina from riders and their horses or ponies. Your dressage test is marked normally (see page 29), then converted into penalty points (so the lower your score the better). Your show jumping and cross-country scores are added to your dressage score. The rider with the lowest overall score wins.

RIDING A TEST

When you ride a test, your performance will be watched closely by the judge. He or she will usually sit in a car behind the C marker. The arena will be marked out by low white boards, and it may have tubs of flowers around the outside. Make sure your pony is familiar with these things before you take a test so that he doesn't "spook".

RIDING IN

Before the test begins, you must warm up or "ride in" your pony. This makes sure that his muscles are supple and that he is concentrating properly. The amount of riding in he will need depends on his temperament. An easygoing, placid pony will need about twenty minutes, while a lively, excitable pony may need as much as two hours. Bear in mind the weather too. You'll have to ride him in for longer on a cold, windy day. Begin your riding in session by walking him on a long rein before you move on to any trotting or cantering work.

Boots and bandages can be worn during riding in, but not for the test.

Rules for riding in
* Let other people know you're about to enter the riding-in area by calling out "I'm coming in".
* Walk your pony on the inside track. The outside track is for faster paces.
* Don't halt your pony on the outside track.
* Pass other riders left shoulder to left shoulder.
* Give way to riders doing lateral work.
* If you need to adjust your tack, go outside the riding-in area.

FINAL PREPARATIONS

Aim to finish your riding in about ten minutes before your test is due to start. This will give you time to take off any bandages or boots your pony has been wearing and check his girth. Check your appearance too, then relax for a few moments and collect your thoughts.

RIDING THE TEST

When the rider before you finishes his or her test, start to ride around the outside of the competition arena. When the judge is ready for you to start, he or she will ring a bell or sound the car horn. Tests start at the A marker and finish with a salute to the judge. When you've finished the test, walk your pony back to the A marker, where you should leave the arena.

Tips for the test
* Concentrate hard on what you are doing.
* If one movement goes badly, don't panic, just move calmly onto the next one.
* Don't rush the test.
* Enjoy the movements you do well.
* Make a fuss of your pony after the test.

This rider is saluting correctly, but ideally, her pony should be in a square halt (see page 13).

Saluting
* Halt at the correct marker.
* Look towards the judge.
* Put your reins and whip (if you have one) in one hand (usually the left).
* Drop your other hand down with the palm of your hand facing inwards.
* Nod your head down and up again.
* Count to three before you move off.

HOW TESTS ARE SCORED

The judge gives each movement a mark from 0 (movement not carried out) to 10 (excellent). The rider with the highest number of marks wins the competition (unless it is an event – see page 27). At the end of the competition, you will be given a scoresheet which shows your marks and the judge's comments. The judge will also give you a set of collective marks. These refer to your pony's way of going and your riding skills throughout the test.

In Advanced competitions there are normally several judges. They sit inside a judging box.

ADVANCED DRESSAGE

You can learn a lot from advanced riders, whether you go to see them at a show, or watch them on the television. Advanced dressage ponies have a high degree of collection (see page 16), enabling them to perform the most difficult dressage movements, some of which are described below.

PIAFFE

Piaffe is an extremely advanced dressage movement. The pony trots on the spot with light, springy steps. His hindlegs should be well underneath his body, taking most of his weight.

The pony should keep his legs moving in a regular trotting rhythm, with a clear moment of suspension between each step.

Piaffe involves a high degree of collection.

The toe of the foreleg should be above the fetlock joint of the other foreleg.

PASSAGE

Passage is a very dramatic movement to watch. The pony springs forward in a slow, dancing trot. The moment of suspension between each stride is long and the

pony's steps are high. Passage should be a smooth movement showing the pony's contained energy. Any jerkiness is considered a serious fault.

Horses and ponies which can perform passage will have reached the highest level of obedience and collection.

FLYING CHANGES

A flying change involves the pony changing his leading leg in canter, during the moment of suspension (see page 8), rather than through walk or trot. Flying changes are a real challenge to both the pony and the rider because they require split-second timing. The rider must give clear, firm aids at exactly the right moment, while the pony must understand instantly what he is being asked to do.

This pony and rider are beginning to work on flying changes. They need to keep the same rhythm and speed.

CANTER PIROUETTE

In canter pirouette, the pony canters around his hindlegs in a half or full circle, without moving forwards. The pony should take high, collected steps, and his hindquarters should be visibly lower than his forehand. Canter pirouettes are extremely hard work for a pony, so he needs to have well-developed muscles and excellent balance. The pony should keep the correct sequence of footfalls and a steady rhythm as he carries out the pirouette.

This horse and rider are performing a canter pirouette in the World Equestrian Games.

INDEX

With thanks to Holly Acuta and Polly, Sally Crisp and Top Gun, Ciara
Gourley and Nula, Kylie Holland and Cnapaton Rosewood, Tarn
Holland and Princess Leya, Sophie Hyde and Moonlight Trickster,
Joe Parker and Harry Houdini.